New Ships

An Anthology of West Indian Poems for Secondary Schools

Edited by Donald G Wilson

Oxford University Press, Ely House, London W. 1

Glasgow New York Toronto Melbourne Wellington
Cape Town Ibadan Nairobi Dar es Salaam Lusaka Addis Ababa
Delhi Bombay Calcutta Madras Karachi Lahore Dacca
Kuala Lumpur Singapore Hong Kong Tokyo

This anthology was first published in 1971
by Savacou Publications Ltd., Kingston, Jamaica.

Reprinted 1975

Set by Hope Services, Wantage, and
printed in Great Britain by
T. H. Brickell & Son Ltd, The Blackmore Press,
Gillingham, Dorset

Cover illustration based on a painting of **Portuguese** caravels,
reproduced by permission of the National Maritime Museum,
Greenwich, England.

We should like to thank the following for permission to reproduce
illustrations: Colin Garland, p.71; Jamaica Tourist Board, pp. 34,
92; Maria LaYacona, p.64; Rose Murray, p.24; Tony Russell,
pp. 40, 62; Cecil Ward, pp. 12, 85.

To the teachers and pupils in our schools

Compiled by
Joseph Belisle, B.A., Dip. Ed.
Meta Bogle, B.A., Dip. Ed.
Jacqueline Briscoe, B.A., Dip. Ed.
Nicholas Darlington, B.A., Dip. Ed.
Hyacinth Campbell, B.A., Dip. Ed.
David A. King, B.A., Dip. Ed.
Michael Lewis, B.A., Dip. Ed.
Keith Lowe, M.A., Ph.D.
Donald Wilson, M.A., Dip. Ed., Dip. Eng. F.L.

Foreword

A novel and welcome feature of this anthology of West Indian verse for schools is that it has been compiled by a team of teachers and educationists. The advantages of this situation are manifold.

Most anthologies represent one man's taste in each instance. The almost inevitable idiosyncrasies of selection allow for an equally idiosyncratic response on the part of the individual reader or teacher. Each enthusiastic teacher of poetry finds himself wanting to compile his own anthology. The team effort behind the present anthology and the fact that it is aimed at a particular set of teachers and students maximize the chances that it will, within its acknowledged limits, satisfy the needs of those at whom it is aimed.

The specificity of aim is in itself most commendable. An anthology aimed broadly at school-children as well as at the layman, and having at the same time tacit hopes of approximating to a comprehensive or definitive anthology of West Indian verse, runs the risk of being neither one thing nor the other. The present compilers have their sights clearly set: the 7th, 8th, and 9th grades of Jamaican Secondary schools. This approach has the virtues of humility, precision, and good sense, without the vice of chauvinism. Given the aims stated, it is natural that the majority of poems should be Jamaican, but not to any unreasonable extent. The anthology remains, after all, an anthology of West Indian verse; and perhaps the present approach to this area of study might be profitably copied in all parts of the West Indies. It seems logical that the learning process should begin with concentration on the child's immediate environment and then move gradually outwards.

So while this anthology does not have, does not claim to have much chance of being the best anthology of West Indian verse, it argues a welcome professionalism on the part of its compilers, a professionalism which is not an outstanding feature of education in the West Indies. The teacher would not presume to tell the poet how to write poetry or what to write; similarly, we do not presume to tell the teacher how to teach poetry or what to teach.

The present compilers have as one of their chief and most desireable criteria that the poems should be 'teachable' to the particular students, and these poems are eminently so. They offer rich possibilities to the teacher, by way of comparison and contrast, their relationship to other areas of study such as West Indian history and geography, and their usefulness in illustrating some of the peculiar features of the West Indian language situation, which is itself an immediate challenge to the teacher. Ultimately an anthology such as this one should help to foster among Jamaicans an awareness of the potential importance of poetry in human life. But this will not happen until the whole examination system in our schools is structured in specific relationship to our particular conditions of life. Many of us can recall having broken away, often secretly, from the English anthologies in order to introduce a West Indian poem or two in the lower forms of secondary schools, only to have to abandon the adventure in frustration in order to cram the students for foreign based examinations. All that will have to be changed.

Edward Baugh,
Senior Lecturer,
Department of English,
University of the West Indies,
Mona.

Contents

Foreword
Introduction: to the Student

Acknowledgements

We wish to thank the following for permission to reproduce
copyright poems.

Louise Bennett: three poems reprinted by permission of
Sangster's Book Stores.

Edward Brathwaite: four poems from *Masks* (or *Rights of Passage*
or *Islands*) by Edward Brathwaite; © Oxford University Press,
1968 (or 1967 or 1969), reprinted by permission.

Nicholás Guillén: two poems translated from the Spanish by
G.R. Coulthard, reprinted by permission of Mrs. Helen Coulthard.

Edward Lucie-Smith: two poems from *A Tropical Childhood and
Other Poems* by Edward Lucie-Smith; © Oxford University Press,
1961, used by permission.

Claude McKay: two poems reprinted by permission of
Carl Cowl Esq.

Alma Norman: five poems from *Ballads of Jamaica* by Alma
Norman, reprinted by permission of the Longman Group Ltd.,
London. 'The Curse of Rose Hall' is reprinted by permission of
The Jamaica Gleaner.

Tom Redcam: 'San Gloria' from *Orange Valley and Other Poems*
by Tom Redcam, reprinted by permission of the Pioneer Press.

W. Adolphe Roberts: 'Tropic Storm' from *Poetry for Children*,
reprinted by permission of the Pioneer Press. 'The Cat' from
Voices of Summerland, reprinted by permission of Fowler Wright
Books Ltd.

Dennis Scott: 'Uncle Time' and 'Third World Blues' from *Uncle
Time* by Dennis Scott, reprinted by permission of the University
of Pittsburg Press. 'Bird' reprinted by permission of the author.

Sir John Squire: 'There was an Indian' from *Verse Worth
Remembering*, reprinted by permission of Macmillan, London
and Basingstoke.

Derek Walcott: two poems from *In a Green Night*, reprinted by
permission of Jonathan Cape Ltd.

We also wish to thank the following authors for permission to
reprint their poems.

Raymond Barrow, Vera Bell, George Campbell, H.D. Carberry,
Frank Collymore, Dennis Craig, A.N. Forde, A.L. Hendriks,
K.E. Ingram, Evan Jones, Basil McFarlane, Mervyn Morris,
Daisy Myrie, Barnabas J. Ramon-Fortuné.

Introduction: to the Student

This anthology is intended for students in the first three years of Secondary School. It is therefore divided into three sections. The poems in each section were carefully selected to suit a particular grade level.

Also the poems were chosen with some general themes in mind—

	Grade 7	Grade 8	Grade 9
1 **Who are we?** Ancestors, heroes, myths, workers, brothers	14-26	42-51	66-77
2 Emigration	27-29	57-60	72, 75
3 Nature	30-36	52-56	84, 86, 89
4 Ritual	37	63	88
5 Time/Death/Hereafter			78-83, 90
6 Childhood			79, 80, 87, 91

These themes are either themselves peculiarly West Indian, or else made so by the treatment of the poets, who in all cases, except one, are of the West Indies. There are some brief biographical notes at the end of this book.

It is not being suggested, however, that you should read in school only West Indian poems. It is hoped, of course, that you will find much in the poems of this anthology that is familiar to you, and so perhaps you may more readily understand and enjoy them. In addition, because of your enjoyment of these poems you will be deepening your experience and insight into your primary culture —the culture of your island and of the West Indies. This is of fundamental importance. Nevertheless, a foundation of this sort should be seen as the basic structure upon which you can build and develop with confidence. Experience, like charity, should begin at home, but not end there.

This means, then, that with the guidance of your teachers you should read and enjoy more and more West Indian poems. And also, you should be led to read the poems of other lands, about other people and places. So through the joy of poetry, you may discover your belonging to your island family, your West Indian community, and to the brotherhood of man.

D. G. Wilson

Poems for Grade 7

There was an Indian

14

There was an Indian, who had known no change,
 Who strayed content along a sunlit beach
Gathering shells. He heard a sudden strange
 Commingled noise; looked up; and gasped for speech.
For in the bay, where nothing was before,
 Moved on the sea, by magic, huge canoes,
With bellying cloths on poles, and not one oar,
 And fluttering coloured signs and clambering crews.
And he, in fear, this naked man alone,
 His fallen hands forgetting all their shells,
His lips gone pale, knelt low behind a stone,
 And stared, and saw, and did not understand,
Columbus's doom-burdened caravels
 Slant to the shore, and all their seamen land.

Sir John Squire

San Gloria

Columbus visited St. Ann's Bay, the Santa Gloria of the
Spaniards.

Oh, Captain of wide western seas,
    Where now thy great soul lives, dost thou
Recall San Gloria's spice-censed breeze?

White-sanded curves where serried trees
    Filed backward as thy sharpened prow
Sheared into foam the racing seas?

San Gloria's wood-carved mountain frieze
    In the blue bay is mirrored now,
As when thy white sail wooed the breeze.

The thunder of insurgent seas
    Beats yet the rough reef's ragged brow,
Roaring by green, far-stretching leas;

Yet through the wood the peony flees,
    The yellow guava ripens now,
Rich-hearted ipomea please.

Dost thou remember things like these,
    Hear yet the dark-robed woodlands sough,
Oh, Captain of wide western seas,
Dost thou remember things like these
    Where thy great soul inhabits now?

Tom Redcam

Judgement at Port Royal

Chorus:
A sigh heaves up from the ocean's deep
Where cold green waters their secrets keep
And many men lie long asleep.

The Palisadoes' finger long
Shows naught today of things so wrong
When life was cheap and lust was strong.

Crouched at the finger's very tip
Port Royal beckoned every ship
And held their sailors in her grip.

There lurked the cut-throat buccaneers
Whose swift lean ship each seaman fears
And trembles at the tales he hears.

Thence sped their ships which cut the waves
Laden with gold, o'er their victims' graves.
There merchants came. And there came slaves.

Port Royal! Famed for this thing first:
Of wicked towns by far the worst.
Men gambled there, and killed, and cursed.

Warehouses full of bloody gains,
And murd'rous fights in twisting lanes,
And drunkards' shouts and sufferers' pains.

Port Royal on its spit of sand,
Proud sinner in a heedless land,
All unaware of Fate at hand.

But heavy was the price to pay
For looted towns and helpless prey.
And June the seventh was the day.

The very land refused to bear
The wickedness she flaunted there.
The earthquake caught her unaware.

Sucked down into the vengeful sea
Were streets and shops, and slaves and free.
Some prayed. Some cursed. But none could fle

A shudder and a sighing cry
Arose from those who did not die,
And floated to the shifting sky.

Then weary stillness settled down
Upon the wreck of that proud town.
Gone all its wealth of great renown.

    Chorus

Alma Norman

Cudjoe and the Man from Westmoreland

Chorus:
Cudjoe was a black man,
　Guthrie he was white.
Both of them were brave men;
　Both knew how to fight.

Now Cudjoe has the numbers
　And knows the secret ways
Where cockpits twist and double.
　So for a win he plays.

But Guthrie plots with cunning;
　Defeat alone he fears.
'Our men have done with running
　After seven weary years.

The black man's ways are wiser;
　With lightning speed they strike,
Then slip away and hide, or
　Melt into the night.'

Thus spoke brave Colonel Guthrie
　To his soldiers waiting there.
'Maroon will fight with courage.
　Be brave like them and dare.

Now keep your muskets ready,
　And keep your courage high,
And let your aim be steady.
　Prepare to win — or die.'

Maroons and Cudjoe waited
　The advance of Guthrie's men.
They watched with breath abated
　And prepared to battle them.

Bare sixty men surrounded
    Their secret hiding place,
And when at last they found it
    A battle fierce took place.

With sudden brazen fury
    The Colonel's bugle blew
And spurred by hopes of glory
    His soldiers shot and slew.

Maroons like shadows fought them
    And more than half were slain.
The kindly nightfall caught them
    And they were safe again.

But many men lay dying
    In the long dark lonely night
And the morning sun saw lying
    Both the black dead and the white.

So they signed a truce between them:
    Brave Cudjoe's mountain band
Agreed to live in peace
    With the man from Westmoreland.

    Chorus

Alma Norman

The Curse of Rose Hall

Darkness hangs thick on the haunted air
And a ghostly jury in session there
Lays Annie Palmer's foul deeds bare
     In the ruined rooms of Rose Hall.

Oh white in the daylight the stone walls gleam
And gracious and spacious the vast rooms seem
And the poisons and murderings all a dream,
     And the frightened ghosts of Rose Hall.

But on moonless evenings when Patoo calls
And no clear brightness from heaven falls
Then into the ruins of splendid halls
     Slink the vengeful ghosts of Rose Hall.

Up from its cellars and nameless graves
Slouch husband, and lovers, and strong black slaves.
And she looks in vain for the face that saves.
     But each wants revenge for Rose Hall.

The deadly evidence tolls its bell
As one by one the victims tell
Of how they lived in that witch's hell
     With the wicked Queen of Rose Hall.

Proud Annie hears what they tell about
And she savagely tries to curse them out,
But nobody there can hear her shout.
     For all are dead at Rose Hall.

With fury she listens to their tale
And not for repentance does she pale —
But to know that her obeah could fail,
     And bring her death at Rose Hall.

When the last of the shuddering victims spoke
The jury its ghostly silence broke,
And bound the White Witch with a fearful yoke
    To the ruined stones of Rose Hall.

Now on secret nights when the sky is blind
And Patoo mocks what his sharp eyes find
You can hear Annie's bitter sobs behind
    The crumbling walls of Rose Hall.

Alma Norman

Ballad of Sixty-Five

The roads are rocky and the hills are steep,
The macca scratches and the gully's deep.
The town is far, news travels slow.
And the mountain men have far to go.

Bogle took his cutlass at Stony Gut
And looked at the small heap of food he'd got
And he shook his head, and his thoughts were sad,
'You can wuk like a mule but de crop still bad'.

Bogle got his men and he led them down
Over the hills to Spanish Town.
They chopped their way and they made a track
To the Governor's house. But he sent them back.

As they trudged home back to Stony Gut
Paul's spirit sank with each bush he cut,
For he thought of the hungry St. Thomas men
Who were waiting for the message he'd bring to them.

They couldn't believe that he would fail
And their anger rose when they heard his tale.
Then they told Paul Bogle of Morant Bay
And the poor man fined there yesterday.

Then Bogle thundered, 'This thing is wrong.
They think we weak, but we hill men strong.
Rouse up yourself. We'll march all night
To the Vestry house, and we'll claim our right.'

The Monday morning was tropic clear
As the men from Stony Gut drew near,
Clenching their sticks in their farmer's hand
To claim their rights in their native land.

Oh many mourned and many were dead
That day when the vestry flames rose red.
There was chopping and shooting and when it done
Paul Bogle and his men knew they had to run.

They ran for the bush where they hoped to hide
But the soldiers poured in from Kingston side.
They took their prisoners to Morant Bay
Where they hanged them high in the early day.

Paul Bogle died but his spirit talks
Anywhere in Jamaica that freedom walks,
Where brave men gather and courage thrills
As it did in those days in St. Thomas hills.

Alma Norman

Ballad of an Old Woman

There was an old woman who never was wed;
Of twenty-one children was she brought to bed,
              Singing Glory to God.

She gave them all her poor means could afford
And brought them all up in the Fear of the Lord,
              Singing Glory to God.

As soon as they grew up, each sailed away,
One after the other, to the great U.S.A.,
              Singing Glory to God.

Sometimes they thought of her, sometimes they wrote
Sometimes they sent her a Five Dollar Note:
              Singing Glory to God.

And when in the course of the long waiting years
The letters ceased coming, she dried her tears,
              Singing Glory to God.

And when the old shed-roof collapsed from decay
She went to the Almshouse and walked all the way,
              Singing Glory to God.

And there she mothered many motherless brats
Who slept on her shoulder and pulled at her plaits,
              Singing Glory to God.

Then one day she sickened and next day she died;
They brought out the hearse and put her inside
              Singing Glory to God.

Only weeds and nettles spring up from her clay
Who is one with the Night and the Light of the Day.
              Singing Glory to God.

Frank Collymore

Revolt of Chief Tacky

Tacky the chieftain decided to fight.
    'I finish with being a slave.'
The morning sun rose clear and bright
    On him and his followers brave.
        (His hundreds of followers brave.)

So cunningly he laid his plan
    So fierce his courage shone,
That up and down Jamaica land
    Men made his cause their own.
        (They made his cause their own.)

But one, faint-hearted, slipped away
    Upon that fateful morn,
And many died on that sad day,
    For soldiers had been warned.
        (Militia men were warned.)

Oh sad it is to have to tell
    But some the challenge spurned.
Once more, like slaves, their spirits fell;
    To bondage they returned.
        (To bondage they returned.)

But Coromantyne Tacky fought,
    'As long as I have breath
No man shall boast that I was caught.'
    A bullet caused his death.
        (Davy's bullet caused his death.)

A bitter bullet laid him low.
    No man knows where he lies.
So sing a mournful song and low
    Beneath Jamaica skies.
        (For in this soil he lies.)

Alma Norman

Noh Lickle Twang!

(Not even a little accent)

Me glad fe se's you come back bwoy,
    But lawd yuh let me dung,
Me shame o' yuh soh till all o'
    Me proudness drop a grung.

Yuh mean yuh goh dah 'Merica
    An spen six whole mont' deh,
An come back not a piece betta
    Dan how yuh did goh wey?

Bwoy yuh noh shame? Is soh you come?
    Afta yuh tan soh lang!
Not even lickle language bwoy?
    Not even little twang?

An yuh sista wat work ongle
    One week wid 'Merican
She talk so nice now dat we have
    De jooce fe undastan?

Bwoy yuh couldn' improve yuhself!
    An yuh get soh much pay?
Yuh spen six mont' a foreign, an
    Come back ugly same way?

Not even a drapes trouziz? or
    A pass de rydim coat?
Bwoy not even a gole teet or
    A gole chain roun yuh t'roat.

Suppose me las' me pass go introjooce
    Yuh to a stranga
As me lamented son wat lately
    Come from 'Merica!

Dem hooda laugh afta me, bwoy
    Me could'n tell dem soh!
Dem hooda sey me lie, yuh was
    A-spen time back a Mocho.

Noh back-ansa me bwoy, yuh talk
    Too bad; shet up yuh mout,
Ah doan know how yuh an yuh puppa
    Gwine to meck it out.

Ef yuh want please him meck him tink
    Yuh bring back someting new.
Yuh always call him 'Pa', dis evenin'
    Wen him come sey 'Poo'.

Louise Bennett

The Lament of the Banana Man

Gal, I'm tellin' you, I'm tired fo' true,
Tired of Englan', tired o' you.
But I can' go back to Jamaica now ...

I'm here in Englan', I'm drawin' pay,
I go to de underground every day—
Eight hours is all, half-hour fo' lunch,
M' uniform's free, an' m' ticket punch—
Punchin' tickets not hard to do,
When I'm tired o' punchin', I let dem through.

I get a paid holiday once a year.
Ol' age an' sickness can' touch me here.

I have a room o' m' own, an' a iron bed,
Dunlopillo under m' head,
A Morphy-Richards to warm de air,
A formica table, an easy chair.
I have summer clothes, an' winter clothes,
An' paper kerchiefs to blow m' nose.

My yoke is easy, my burden is light,
I know a place I can go to, any night.
Dis place Englan'! I'm not complainin',
If it col', it col', if it rainin', it rainin'.
I don' mind' if it's mostly night,
Dere's always inside, or de sodium light.

I don' min' white people starin' at me
Dey don' want me here? Don't is deir country?
You won' catch me bawlin' any homesick tears
If I don' see Jamaica for a t'ousand years!

... Gal, I'm tellin' you, I'm tired fo' true,
Tired of Englan', tired o' you,
I can' go back to Jamaica now—
But I'd want to die there, anyhow.

Evan Jones

Nature

We have neither Summer nor Winter
Neither Autumn nor Spring.
We have instead the days
When the gold sun shines on the lush green canefields—
Magnificently.
The days when the rain beats like bullets on the roofs
And there is no sound but the swish of water in the gullies
And trees struggling in the high Jamaica winds.
Also there are the days when leaves fade from off guango trees
And the reaped canefields lie bare and fallow to the sun.
But best of all there are the days when the mango and the
    logwood blossom
When the bushes are full of the sound of bees and the scent of
    honey,
When the tall grass sways and shivers to the slightest breath of
    air,
When the buttercups have paved the earth with yellow stars
And beauty comes suddenly and the rains have gone.

H. D. Carberry

North and South

O sweet are tropic lands for waking dreams
    There time and life move lazily along.
There by the banks of blue and silver streams
    Grass-sheltered crickets chirp incessant song;
Gay-coloured lizards loll all through the day,
    Their tongues out-stretched for careless little flies.

And swarthy children in the fields at play,
    Look upward, laughing at the smiling skies.
A breath of idleness is in the air
    That casts a subtle spell upon all things,
And love and mating-time are everywhere,
    And wonder to life's commonplace clings.

The fluttering humming-bird darts through the trees,
    And dips his long beak in the big bell-like flowers.
The leisured buzzard floats upon the breeze,
    Riding a crescent cloud for endless hours.
The sea beats softly on the emerald strands—
    O sweet for quiet dreams are tropic lands.

Claude McKay

Tropic Storm

The scent of jasmines in the sultry air,
    A deathly stillness hanging over all,
Great sombre clouds, which float across the sky
    And hide the sun, as with a funeral pall.
The birds' sweet voices silenced in the trees,
    As if they had not got the heart to sing,
As on some twig, close-sheltered by the leaves,
    Each sits with ruffled plumes and drooping wing.
But now a sullen murmur breaks the calm,
    The gathering East Wind stirs the vapours warm,
The roll of thunder smites upon the ear,
    The lightning flashes red—and bursts the storm.

W. Adolphe Roberts
(Written at the age of fifteen)

Litany

I hold the splendid daylight in my hands
Inwardly grateful for a lovely day.
Thank you life.
Daylight like a fine fan spread from my hands,
Daylight like scarlet poinsettias.
Daylight like yellow cassia flowers
Daylight like clean water
Daylight like green cacti
Daylight like sea sparkling with white horses
Daylight like sunstrained blue sky
Daylight like tropic hills
Daylight like a sacrament in my hands.
Amen.

George Campbell

But Those Unheard

From where I sit I see a patch
Of sky, but chiefly trees;
A lovely thing to view their green
Within the window-frame:
Not only green of varying tone
Beneath the dominant blue,
But blossoms burning in the green
Chanting their secret song.
Along the lignumvitae shine
Clusters of tender mauve;
Above, against the sky, bright stars
Of frangipani glow,
And scarlet bougainvillea throbs
From out the deepest green.
A lovely thing to see all this
Within the window-frame —
The long blue archway of the sky,
The music of the trees,
To let the senses sink within
This silent symphony.

Frank Collymore

Sheep

God made sheep in the early morning.

In his hands he caught the clusters
Of the fleecy clouds of dawning
And tied them in bunches
And fastened their feet and their noses
With wet brown clay
And into their eyes he dropped
With reeds from a nearby river
The light of the dying morning star
And the light of the dying moon.

And then on that creation morning
When the sun had flooded the peaks and plains
And the dew lay thick on the rushes
Man saw sheep on the grazing grass
And heard the sadness of their bleating.

K. E. Ingram

Sensemaya:
A Chant for Killing a Snake

Mayombe-bombe-mayombé!
Mayombe-bombe-mayombé!
Mayombe-bombe-mayombé!

The snake has eyes of glass;
the snake comes and coils itself round a pole;
with his eyes of glass, round a pole,
with his eyes of glass.
The snake walks without legs;
the snake hides in the grass;
walking he hides in the grass
walking without legs.

Mayombe-bombe-mayombé!
Mayombe-bombe-mayombé!
Mayombe-bombe-mayombé!

If you hit him with an axe he will die.
Hit him hard!
Do not hit him with your foot, he will bite,
do not hit him with your foot, he is going away!

Sensemayá, the snake.
Sensemayá,
Sensemayá, with his eyes,
Sensemayá.
Sensemayá, with his tongue,
Sensemayá.
Sensemayá, with his mouth,
Sensemayá —

Dead snake cannot eat;
dead snake cannot hiss;
cannot walk
cannot run.
Dead snake cannot look;
dead snake cannot drink,
cannot breathe,
cannot bite.

Mayombe-bombe-mayombé!
Sensemayá, the snake —
Mayombe-bombe-mayombé!
Sensemayá, it is still —
Mayombe-bombe-mayombé!
Sensemayá, the snake —
Mayombe-bombe-mayombé!
Sensemayá, it is dead.

Nicolás Guillén
(trans. G. R. Coulthard)

Poems for Grade 8

Ancestor on the Auction Block

Ancestor on the auction block
Across the years your eyes seek mine
Compelling me to look.
I see your shackled feet
Your primitive black face
I see your humiliation
And turn away
Ashamed.

Across the years your eyes seek mine
Compelling me to look
Is this mean creature that I see
Myself?
Ashamed to look
Because of myself ashamed
Shackled by my own ignorance
I stand
A slave.

Humiliated
I cry to the eternal abyss
For understanding
Ancestor on the auction block
Across the years your eyes meet mine
Electric
I am transformed
My freedom is within myself.

I look you in the eyes and see
The spirit of God eternal
Of this only need I be ashamed
Of blindness to the God within me
The same God who dwelt within you
The same eternal God
Who shall dwell
In generations yet unborn.

Ancestor on the auction block

Across the years
I look
I see you sweating, toiling, suffering
Within your loins I see the seed
Of multitudes
From your labour
Grow roads, aqueducts, cultivation
A new country is born
Yours was the task to clear the ground
Mine be the task to build.

Vera Bell

History Makers

Women stone breakers
Hammers and rocks
Tired child makers
Haphazard frocks
Strong thigh
Rigid head
Bent nigh
Hardwhite piles
Of stone
Under hot sky
In the gully bed
No smiles
No sigh
No moan.

Women child bearers
Pregnant frocks
Wilful toil sharers
Destiny shapers
Hammers and rocks.

George Campbell

Road-Mending

Patches of black
In the pitch
Make the most
Unusual patterns:
Irregular blocks,
Birds' wings,
Shapes of ships,
Animals' heads,
Curiously
Interfigured.

This is the
Road-mender's art:
With tar and gravel
To design
A dozen or more
Shapes and figures;
To figure out
From fancy only
How to inlay
Gravel and tar . . . .

Barnabas J. Ramon-Fortuné

Song of the Banana Man

Tourist, white man wiping his face,
Met me in Golden Grove market place.
He looked at my old clothes brown with stain
And soaked right through with the Portland rain.
He cast his eye, and turned up his nose
And said, 'You're a beggar man I suppose,'
He said, 'Boy get some occupation,
Be of some value to your nation.'

I said, 'By God and this big right hand
You must recognise a banana man.'

Up in the hills where the streams are cool,
Where mullet and janga swim in the pool,
I have ten acres of mountain side
And a dainty foot donkey that I ride
Four Gros Michel and four Lacatan
Some coconut trees and some hills of yam
And I pasture on that very same land
Five she goats and a big black ram.

That, by God and this big right hand
Is the property of the banana man.

I leave my yard early morning time
And set my foot to the mountain climb
I bend my back for the hot-sun toil
And my cutlass rings on the stony soil,
Clearing and weeding, digging and planting,
Till Massa sun drop back a John Crow mountain
Then home again in cool evening time
Perhaps whistling this little rhyme,

Praise God and this big right hand
I will live and die a banana man.

Banana day is my special day
I cut my stems and I'm on my way
Load up the donkey, leave the land
Head down the hill to banana stand,
When the truck comes down I take a ride
All the way down to the harbour side;
That is the night when you tourist man
Would change your place with a banana man.

Yes, praise God and my big right hand
I will live and die a banana man.

The bay is calm and the moon is bright
The hills look black though the sky is light
Down at the dock is an English ship
Resting after her ocean trip
While on the pier is a monstrous hustle
Tally men, carriers all in a bustle
With the stems on their heads in a long black snake
Some singing the songs that banana men make.

Like Praise God and my big right hand
I will live and die a banana man.

Then the payment comes and we have some fun
Me, Zekiel, Breda and Duppy Son
Down at the bar near United wharf,
Knock back a white rum, bus' a laugh
Fill the empty bag for further toil
With saltfish, breadfruit and coconut oil
Then head back home to my yard to sleep
A proper sleep that is long and deep.

Yes, praise God and my big right hand
I will live and die a banana man.

So when you see these old clothes brown with stain
And soaked clean through with Portland rain
Don't cast your eyes nor turn your nose
Don't judge a man by his patchy clothes
I'm a strong man a proud man and I'm free
Part of these mountains part of this sea
I know myself and I know my ways
And will say with pride to the end of my days,

Praise God and my big right hand
I will live and die a banana man.

Evan Jones

Market Women

Down from the hills, they come
With swinging hips and steady stride
To feed the hungry Town
They stirred the steep dark land
To place within the growing seed.
And in the rain and sunshine
Tended the young green plants,
They bred, and dug and reaped.
And now, as Heaven has blessed their toil,
They come, bearing the fruits,
These hand-maids of the Soil,
Who bring full baskets down,
To feed the hungry Town.

Daisy Myrie

Road to Lacovia

This is a long, forbidding road, a narrow,
hard aisle of asphalt under
a high gothic arch of bamboos.
Along it a woman drags a makeshift barrow
in slanting rain, and thunder:
a thin woman who wears no shoes.

This is St. Elizabeth, a hard parish
to work; but when you are born
on land, you want to work that land.
Nightfall comes here swift and harsh and deep, but garish
flames of lightning show up torn
cheap clothing barely patched, and

a face patterned by living. Every sharp line
of this etching has the mark
of struggle. To the eye, unyielding
bleak earth has brought her close to famine;
yet through this wild descent of dark
this woman dares to walk, and sing.

A. L. Hendriks

When I Pray

Dark peoples
Singing in my veins
Fair peoples
Singing in soft strains.

O when I lift my hand and pray
I bow with blue eyes
Dark hands
Red hair.

My prayer is life,
O mother and child
In the end
O mother and child.

George Campbell

The Cat

Pleasures that I most enviously sense,
    Pass in long ripples down her flanks and stir
    The plume that is her tail. She deigns to purr
And take caresses. But her paws would tense
To flashing weapons at the least offence.
    Humbly I bend to stroke her silken fur,
    I am content to be a slave to her
I am enchanted by her insolence.

No one of all the women I have known
    Has been so beautiful, or proud, or wise
    As this Angora with her amber eyes.
She makes her chosen cushion seem a throne,
    And wears the same voluptuous, slow smile
    She wore when she was worshipped on the Nile.

W. Adolphe Roberts

Minute's Magic

The asphalt square in the courtyard thronged
　　By the shiftless crowd, spurned
By the shifting feet, lies barren, bare
　　(How long since green things burned
Here? How long since blossoms burst
　　From its fettered heart?), drab
As the feet that scrape and traipse and stamp
　　Over the tettered scab.
And then a pelting stinging shower;
　　The crowd scatters and the rain
Lashing the metalled surface makes
　　Beauty live again.
Here as each shaft of rain strikes home
　　Mark what ghost flowers spring
Up from it. What words, what art
　　Describe their patterning?
Bells of water air and light
　　Unfold, expand and fall
To rise again petal upon petal;
　　A myriad dancing small
Rain flowers, rain fairies
　　Leaping, sparkling run
With waving arms and tossing heads
　　Catching the threads of sun
To weave a pattern diamonded;
　　Flower bubbles, frail
Crystal goblets, lilies spun
　　From glass ephemeral,
They bloom, they dance, they shine, and each
　　As individual
As you or I. Close the eyes
　　Quick with a flick like the shutter
Of a cinecamera: work that trick
　　Let the eyelids blink and stutter
And capture one, just one, ere the shower
　　Stops; let one remain
On the memory's screen when the asphalt square
　　Is bare and blank again.

Frank Collymore

Flame-Heart

So much have I forgotten in ten years,
So much in ten brief years! I have forgot
What time the purple apples come to juice,
And what month brings the shy forget-me-not.
I have forgot the special, startling season
Of the pimento's flowering and fruiting;
What time of year the ground doves brown the fields
And fill the noonday with their curious fluting.
    I have forgotten much, but still remember
    The poinsettia's red, blood-red, in warm December.

I still recall the honey-fever grass,
But cannot recollect the high days when
We rooted them out of the ping-wing path
To stop the mad bees in the rabbit pen.
I often try to think in what sweet month
The languid painted ladies used to dapple
The yellow by-road mazing from the main,
Sweet with the golden threads of the rose-apple.
    I have forgotten — strange — but quite remember
    The poinsettia's red, blood-red, in warm December.

What weeks, what months, what time of the mild year
We cheated school to have our fling at tops?
What days our wine-thrilled bodies pulsed with joy
Feasting upon blackberries in the copse?
Oh some I know! I have embalmed the days,
Even the sacred moments when we played,
All innocent of passion, uncorrupt,
At noon and evening in the flame-heart's shade.
    We were so happy, happy, I remember,
    Beneath the poinsettia's red in warm December.

Claude McKay

Flowers

I have never learnt the names of flowers.
From beginning, my world has been a place
Of pot-holed streets where thick, sluggish gutters race
In slow time, away from garbage heaps and sewers
Past blanched old houses around which cowers
Stagnant earth. There, scarce green thing grew to chase
The dull-grey squalor of sick dust; no trace
Of plant save few sparse weeds; just these, no flowers.

One day, they cleared a space and made a park
There in the city's slums; and suddenly
Came stark glory like lightning in the dark,
While perfume and bright petals thundered slowly.
I learnt no names, but hue, shape and scent mark
My mind, even now, with symbols holy.

Dennis Craig

Elegy

Greengold the leaves,
    The setting sun staining
The patch of shrubbery
    With light; the light waning
Elsewhere: all else dull
    And grey against the fire.
Greengold each stem,
    A burning golden wire,
And scarlet blossoms tongues
    Of flame. But while I write
The light fails; scarlet
    And green goldbright
Fade; tree and shrub
    And blossom shrink and are
Lost in the dusk; only
    A gleaming scimitar
Cleaving the evening sky
    With greengold light
Swift-sheathed. The blinds are drawn
    And the landscape sinks to night.

Frank Collymore

Jamaica Wanderers

You'll find us in Nigeria. you'll see us in Colon
To Ghana and Liberia Jamaica men have gone.

When they had a job to finish and they couldn't manage, then
The call went out for workers and they got Jamaica men.

We've built a mighty railway, cut that ditch through Panama,
Planted cane and cut banana. Where there's work, that's where
    we are.

We sometimes went as teachers, or as farmers, or as wives.
We sometimes went as nurses. And we sometimes lost our lives.

Remember Mary Seacole, most famous of us all?
She comforted the soldiers wounded at Sevastopol.

Oh some of us were artisans, and something lit a spark,
So East and South and North and West you'll find we've made
    our mark.

We've braved the frozen Northern snow, the steamy tropic rain.
Oh anywhere you care to go — You'll find Jamaica men.

Alma Norman

The Emigrants

So you have seen them
with their cardboard grips,
felt hats, rain-
cloaks, the women
with their plain
or purple-tinted
coats hiding their fatten-
ed hips.

These are The Emigrants.
On sea-port quays
at air-ports
anywhere where there is ship
or train, swift
motor car, or jet
to travel faster than the breeze
you see them gathered:
passports stamped
their travel papers wrapped
in old disused news-
papers: lining their patient queues.

Where to?
They do not know.
Canada, the Panama
Canal, the Miss-
issippi painfields, Florida?
or on to dock
at hissing smoke locked
Glasgow?

Why do they go?
They do not know.
Seeking a job
they settle for the very best
the agent has to offer,
jabbing a neighbour
out of work for four bob
less a week.

What do they hope for
what find there
these New World mariners
Columbus coursing kaffirs

What Cathay shores
for them are gleaming golden
what magic keys they carry to unlock
what gold endragoned doors?

Edward Brathwaite

Colonisation in Reverse

Wat a joyful news, Miss Mattie,
    I feel like me heart gwine burs'
Jamaica people colonizin
    Englan in reverse.

By de hundred, by de t'ousan
    From country and from town,
By de ship-load, by de plane-load
    Jamaica is Englan boun.

Dem a-pour out o' Jamaica,
    Everybody future plan
Is fe get a big-time job
    An settle in de mother lan.

What a islan! What a people!
    Man an woman, old an young
Jusa pack dem bag an baggage
    An tun history upside dung!

Some people don't like travel,
    But fe show dem loyalty
Dem all a-open up cheap-fare-
    To-Englan agency.

An week by week dem shippin off
    Dem countryman like fire,
Fe immigrate an populate
    De seat o' de Empire

Oonoo see how life is funny,
    Ooonoo see de tunabout,
Jamaica live fe box bread
    Outa English people mout'.

For wen dem catch a Englan,

    An start play dem different role,
Some will settle down to work
    An some will settle fe de dole.

Jane say de dole is not too bad
    Because dey payin' she
Two pounds a week fe seek a job
    Dat suit her dignity.

Me say Jane will never find work
    At the rate how she dah-look,
For all day she stay pon Aunt Fan couch
    An read love-story book.

Wat a devilment a Englan!
    Dem face war an brave de worse,
But I'm wonderin' how dem gwine stan'
    Colonizin' in reverse.

Louise Bennett

The Making of the Drum

The Skin

First the goat
must be killed
and the skin
stretched.

Bless you, four-footed animal, who eats rope,
skilled
upon rocks, horned with our sin;
stretch your skin, stretch

it tight on our hope;
we have killed
you to make a thin
voice that will reach

further than hope
further than heaven, that will
reach deep down to our gods where the thin
light cannot leak, where our stretched

hearts cannot leap. Cut the rope
of its throat, skilled
destroyer of goats; its sin,
spilled on the washed gravel, reaches

and spreads to devour us all. So the goat
must be killed
and its skin
stretched.

Edward Brathwaite

Poems for Grade 9

Ballad of My Two Grandfathers

Shadows that only I can see
my two grandfathers go with me.

Lance with head of bone
drum of leather and of wood:
my black grandfather.

Ruff round his broad throat,
grey warrior's armour:
my white grandfather.

Naked foot, body of rock,
these from my black man;
pupils of Antarctic glass,
these from my white man.

Africa of dank forests
and heavy, muffled gongs —
I am dying
　　　　　(says my black grandfather)
Black water of crocodiles,
green morning of coco palms.
I am weary
　　　　　(says my white grandfather)
O sails of bitter wind
galleon burning gold.
I am dying
　　　　　(says my black grandfather)
O coasts of virgin throats
cheated with glass trinkets.
I am weary
　　　　　(says my white grandfather)

O pure sun of beaten gold,
caught in the hoop of the tropics
O pure moon so round and clear
over the sleep of monkeys.

How many ships! How many ships!
How many Negroes! How many Negroes!
What long refulgence of sugar-cane!
What lashes those of the slave-trader!
Blood? Blood! Tears? Tears!
Half-opened veins and eye-lids
and empty day-breaks
and sunsets on plantations
and a great voice, a strong voice
shattering the silence.
And O the ships, so many ships,
so many Negroes.

      Shadows that only I can see
      my two grandfathers go with me.

Don Federico shouts to me
and Taita Facundo is silent;
and both dream on through the night,
I bring them together.
                  Federico.
Facundo. They both embrace.
They both sigh. They both
raise their proud heads
under the high stars
both of the same stature
black anguish and white anguish
Both of the same stature.
And they shout. And dream. And weep. And sing.
And sing — and sing — and sing.

             Nicolás Guillén
          (trans. G. R. Coulthard)

Third World Blues

I go among the fashionable drums
trying to keep true my own blood's subtle beat.
Something of darkness here, of jazz-horn heat,
but something too of minuet; it hums
cool in my voice, measures my heart, my feet
strictly. And not all the blues, the concrete
jungles of this Third World, mine, can defeat
that pale and civil music when it comes.

So I make my own new way; I entreat
no tribal blessing or honour. I build —
lonely a little — my house. It is filled
with ghosts, with their summoning air, I greet
them all; their tunes, their joys mine. I advance,
my feet bare to a strangely patterned dance.

Dennis Scott

Holy

Holy be the white head of a Negro.
Sacred be the black flax of a black child.
Holy be
The golden down
That will stream in the waves of the winds
And will thin like dispersing cloud.
Holy be
Heads of Chinese hair
Sea calm sea impersonal
Deep flowering of the mellow and traditional.
Heads of peoples fair
Bright shimmering from the riches of their species;
Heads of Indians
With feeling of distance and space and dusk:
Heads of wheaten gold,
Heads of peoples dark
So strong so original:
All of the earth and the sun!

George Campbell

Deeper than Blood

Who are we the tawny ones?
Sun-fires, dawn-red, noon-orange,
break in our skin under dusk-shadow
lighting the sepia with intense saffrons.

Are we acceptable to black, and white?
For we are neither, our synthesis
is more subtle. Are both suspicious?
Finding us so dark! So light!

Are we not blended and caught from old
pigments? What new crucible heats
and fuses our proud mixture? Where
are our colours burnt? In what bright mould?

Have we not taken ebonys and crimsons,
ochres and pale ecrus of loves
deeper than blood for the making of
our harmonies? We the tawny ones.

A. L. Hendriks

The New Ships

1

Takoradi was hot.
Green struggled through red
as we landed.

Laterite lanes drifted off
into dust
into silence.

Mammies crowded with cloths,
flowered and laughed;
white teeth
smooth voices like pebbles
moved by the sea of their language.

Akwaaba they smiled
meaning welcome

akwaaba they called
aye kooo

well have you walked
have you journeyed

welcome.

You who have come
back a stranger
after three hundred years

welcome.

Here is a stool for
you; sit; do
you remember?

Here is water
dip
wash your hands
are you ready
to eat?

Here is plantain
here palm oil:
red, staining the fingers;
good for the heat,
for the sweat.

Do
you remember?

2

I tossed my net
but the net caught
no fish

I dipped a wish
but the well
was dry

Beware
beware
beware

I travelled to a distant town
I could not find my mother
I could not find my father
I could not hear the drum

Whose ancestor am I?

I walked in the bush
but my cut-
lass cut
no path;
returned
from the farm
but could not hear
my children laugh.

Beware
beware
beware

For now the long hot flint-
locks sing with heat;
fever of quick sales
rot the branches

of bone; blood brands the bird's
full sails and trinkets
sear my flesh. Whose
brother, now, am I?

Could these soft huts
have held me?
Wattle daubed on wall,
straw-hatted roofs,

seen my round or-
dering, when kicked to life
I cried
to the harsh light around me?

If you should see someone
coming this way
send help, send help, send help
for I am up to my eyes in fear.

Edward Brathwaite

Back to Africa

Back to Africa Miss Matty?
Yuh noh know wha yuh dah-sey?
Yuh haffe come from some weh fus,
Before yuh go back deh?

Me know sey dat yuh great great great
Gramma was African,
But Matty, doan yuh great great great
Grampa was Englishman?

Den yuh great granmada fada
By yuh fada side was Jew?
An yuh grampa by yuh mada side
Was Frenchie parley-vous!

But de balance o' yuh family
Yuh whole generation
Oonoo all bawn dung a Bun grung
Oonoo all is Jamaican!

Den is weh yuh gwine Miss Matty?
Oh, you view de countenance,
An between yuh an de Africans
Is great resemblance!

Ascorden to dat, all dem blue-y'eye
Wite American,
Who-fa great granpa was Englishman
Mus go back a Englan!

Wat a debil of a bump-an-bore,
Rig-jig and palam-pam!
Ef de whole worl' start fe go back
Weh dem great granpa come from!

Ef a hard time yuh dah-run from
Teck yuh chance, but Matty, do
Sure o' weh yuh come from so yuh got
Someweh fe come-back to!

Go a foreign, seek yuh fortune,
But noh tell nobody sey
Yuh dah-go fe seek yuh homelan
For a right deh so yuh deh!

Louise Bennett

Ancestors

Every Friday morning my grandfather
left his farm of canefields, chickens, cows,
and rattled in his trap down to the harbour town,
to sell his meat. He was a butcher.
Six-foot-three and very neat: high collar,
winged, a grey cravat, a waistcoat, watch-
chain just above the belt, thin narrow-
bottomed trousers, and the shoes his wife
would polish every night. He drove the trap
himself: slap of the leather reins
along the horse's back and he'd be off
with a top-hearted homburg on his head:
black English country gentleman.

Now he is dead. The meat shop burned,
his property divided. A doctor bought
the horse. His mad alsations killed it.
The wooden trap was chipped and chopped
by friends and neighbours and used to stop-
gap fences and for firewood. One yellow
wheel was rolled across the former cowpen gate.
Only his hat is left. I 'borrowed' it.
I used to try it on and hear the night wind
man go battering through the canes, cocks waking up and thinking
it was dawn through the clinking country night.
Great caterpillar tractors clatter down
the broken highway now; a diesel engine grunts
where pigs once hunted garbage.
A thin asthmatic cow shares the untrashed garage.

Edward Brathwaite

Uncle Time

Uncle Time is an ole, ole man ...
All year long 'im wash 'im foot in de sea,
long, lazy years on de wet san'
and shake de coco-nut tree
dem quiet-like wid 'im sea-win' laughter,
scraping away de lan' ...

Uncle Time is a spider-man, cunning an' cool,
him tell yu': watch de hill an' yu' si me,
Huhn! Fe yu' yi no quick enough fe si
how 'im move like mongoose; man, yu' t'ink 'im fool?

Me Uncle Time smile black as sorrow;
'im voice is sof' as bamboo leaf
but Lawd, me Uncle cruel.
When 'im play in de street
wid yu' woman, — watch 'im! By tomorrow
she dry as cane-fire, bitter as cassava; an' when 'im
        teach yu' son, long after
yu' walk wid stranger, an' yu' bread is grief.
Watch how 'im spin web roun' yu' house, an' creep
inside; an' when 'im touch yu', weep.

Dennis Scott

The Day My Father Died

The day my father died
    I could not cry;
My mother cried,
    Not I.

His face on the pillow
    In the dim light
Wrote mourning to me,
    Black and white.

We saw him struggle,
    Stiffen, relax;
The face fell empty,
    Dead as wax.

I'd read of death
    But never seen.
My father's face, I swear,
    Was not serene;

Topple that lie,
    However appealing:
That face was absence
    Of all feeling.

My mother's tears were my tears,
    Each sob shook me:
The pain of death is living,
    The dead are free.

For me my father's death
    Was mother's sorrow;
That day was her day,
    Loss was tomorrow.

Mervyn Morris

The Lesson

'Your father's gone,' my bald headmaster said.
His shiny dome and brown tobacco jar
Splintered at once in tears. It wasn't grief.
I cried for knowledge which was bitterer
Than any grief. For there and then I knew
That grief has uses — that a father dead
Could bind the bully's fist a week or two;
And then I cried for shame, then for relief.

I was a month past ten when I learnt this:
I still remember how the noise was stilled
In school-assembly when my grief came in.
Some goldfish in a bowl quietly sculled
Around their shining prison on its shelf.
They were indifferent. All the other eyes
Were turned towards me. Somewhere in myself
Pride, like a goldfish, flashed a sudden fin.

Edward Lucie-Smith

A Letter from Brooklyn

An old lady writes me in a spidery style,
Each character trembling, and I see a veined hand
Pellucid as paper, travelling on a skein
Of such frail thought its thread is often broken;
Or else the filament from which a phrase is hung
Dims to my sense, but caught, it shines like steel,
As touch a line, and the whole web will feel.
She describes my father, yet I forget her face
More easily than my father's yearly dying;
Of her I remember small, buttoned boots and the place
She kept in our wooden church on those Sundays
Whenever her strength allowed;
Grey haired, thin voiced, perpetually bowed.

'I am Mable Rawlins,' she writes, 'and know both your
    parents';
He is dead, Miss Rawlins, but God bless your tense:
'Your father was a dutiful, honest,
Faithful and useful person.'
For such plain praise what fame is recompense?
'A horn-painter, he painted delicately on horn,
He used to sit around the table and paint pictures.'
The peace of God needs nothing to adorn
It, nor glory nor ambition.
'He is twenty-eight years buried,' she writes,
    'he was called home,
And is, I am sure, doing greater work.'

The strength of one frail hand in a dim room
Somewhere in Brooklyn, patient and assured,
Restores my sacred duty to the Word.
'Home, home,' she can write, with such short time to live,
Alone as she spins the blessings of her years;
Not withered of beauty if she can bring such tears,
Nor withdrawn from the world that breaks its lovers so;
Heaven is to her the place where painters go,
All who bring beauty on frail shell or horn,
There was all made, thence their lux-mundi drawn,
Drawn, drawn, till the thread is resilient steel,
Lost though it seems in darkening periods,
And there they return to do work that is God's.

So this old lady writes, and again I believe.
I believe it all, and for no man's death I grieve.

Derek Walcott

An old Jamaican Woman thinks about the Hereafter

What would I do forever in a big place, who
have lived all my life in a small island?
The same parish holds the cottage I was born in, all
my family, and the cool churchyard.
                    I have looked
up at the stars from my front verandah and have been afraid
of their pathless distances. I have never flown
in the loud aircraft nor have I seen palaces,
so I would prefer not to be taken up high nor
rewarded with a large mansion.
                    I would like
to remain half-drowsing through an evening light
watching bamboo trees sway and ruffle for a valley-wind,
to remember old times but not to live them again;
occasionally to have a good meal with no milk
nor honey for I don't like them, and now and then to walk
by the grey sea-beach with two old dogs and watch
men bring up their boats from the water.
                    For all this,
for my hope of heaven, I am willing to forgive my debtors
and to love my neighbour ...
                    although the wretch throws stones
at my white rooster and makes too much noise in her damn
    backyard.

                                        A. L. Hendriks

Dawn is a Fisherman

Dawn is a fisherman, his harpoon of light
Poised for a throw — so swiftly morning comes:
The darkness squats upon the sleeping land
Like a flung cast-net, and the black shapes of boats
Lie hunched like nesting turtles
On the flat calm of the sea.

Among the trees the houses peep at the stars
Blinking farewell, and half-awakened birds
Hurtle across the vista, some in the distance
Giving their voice self-criticized auditions.

Warning comes from the cocks, their necks distended
Like city trumpeters: and suddenly
Between the straggling fences of grey cloud
The sun, a barefoot boy, strides briskly up
The curved beach of the sky, flinging his greetings
Warmly in all directions, laughingly saying
Up, up, the day is here! Another day is here!

Raymond Barrow

Canes by the Roadside

Time was
you tossed in a delirium
of whispers near the roadside:
now your last whisper
is a treasury of lost sound

Months ago
you were a handful
of green ribbons teasing the wind:
now dead strips tell
where the colour and the sparkle go.

In the cycle

of things you will submit
to the tyranny of shining teeth
and the remorseless murmur of the mill
and all your once-green pride will not console a bit.

Heaped up
in your pyre ready for
the yearly sacrifices to power
you lie robbed of the majesty
of your plotted earth
bared of the eagerness of your dream.

A. N. Forde

Bird

That day the bird hunted an empty, gleaming sky
and climbed and coiled and spun measures of joy,
half-sleeping in the sly wind way
above my friend and me. Oh,
its wings' wind-flick and fleche were free
and easy in the sun, and a whip's tip
tracing of pleasure its mute madrigal,
that I below watched it so tall
it could not fall save slow
down the slow day.

'What is it?' said my friend.
'Yonder ...'
    Hill and home patterned and curved
and frozen in the white round air
'Yes, there,' he said, 'I see it ...'
                up
the steep sky till the eye
lidded from weight of sun on earth and wing!

'Watch this,' he said, bending for stones,
and my boy's throat grew tight with warning
to the bird that rode the feathered morning.

'Now there's a good shot, boy!' he said.
I was only ten then.
'If you see any more be sure to shout
but don't look at the sun too long,' he said,
'makes your eyes run.'

Dennis Scott

Roman Holiday

O, It was a lovely funeral!
    One hundred and thirty-two cars,
And three of them packed high with flowers
And the streets thronged with people —
It reminded me of the Coronation —
And then such a beautiful service:
Organ and full choir of course,
And hardly a dry eye in the chapel.
And there were so many people present that they all couldn't
    get in and ever so many of them had to stand outside
    and during the service there was such a hard shower,
And most of the gentlemen in morning coats and top hats too.
And a well-dressed respectable-looking woman turned to me
And asked me —
Poor creature, she could scarcely articulate the words —
If it was true he'd really died from what we heard,
And I told her it was only too true, poor man.
And it wasn't until afterwards that I discovered
It really wasn't *his* funeral at all.
Because there was another one that evening and they had both
    got mixed up in all the confusion;
And I do think they ought to see to it that better arrangements
    should be made —
I mean, it can put one out so;
And when I did manage to get outside and reach the grave
It was all over.
But it really was a lovely funeral,
And I don't know when I've cried so much.
And that reminds me, my dear:
Have you heard that his youngest daughter
Has run away
With the chauffeur?

Frank Collymore

Tales of the Islands: Chapter X

'adieu foulard ...'

I watched the island narrowing the fine
    Writing of foam around the precipices then
The roads as small and casual as twine
    Thrown on its mountains; I watched till the plane
Turned to the final north and turned above
    The open channel with the grey sea between
The fishermen's islets until all that I love
    Folded in cloud; I watched the shallow green
That broke in places where there would be reef,
    The silver glinting on the fuselage, each mile
Dividing us and all fidelity strained
    Till space would snap it. Then, after a while
I thought of nothing, nothing, I prayed, would change;
    When we set down at Seawell it had rained.

Derek Walcott

The Modern Man

I came
And laughed at my father —
He
with his sideburns
Smelling of bear's grease
His coat
like that of the gentleman
whose image
is on tobacco tins
His watch-chain
And boots!
God!
how ridiculous he looked!

I
With my moustache
like Gable's
My sports coat
like Taylor's
My blue suede shoes

Today
My son came
And laughed at me.

Basil McFarlane

A Tropical Childhood

In the hot noons I heard the fusillade
    As soldiers on the range learnt how to kill,
Used my toy microscope, whose lens arrayed
    The twenty rainbows in a parrot's quill.

Or once, while I was swimming in the bay,
    The guns upon the other, seaward shore
Began a practice-shoot; the angry spray
    Fountained above the point at every roar.

Then I, in the calm water, dived to chase
    Pennies my father threw me, searched the sand
For the brown disc a yard beneath my face,
    And never tried to see beyond my hand.

That was the time when a dead grasshopper
    Devoured by ants before my captive eye
Made the sun dark, yet distant battles were
    Names in a dream, outside geography.

Edward Lucie-Smith

Biographical Notes

Raymond Barrow is a civil servant in Belize. He was born in Belize City in 1920, educated at St. John's College, Belize, and at Cambridge University.

Vera Bell, born in St. Ann, Jamaica, was educated at Wolmer's Girls' School and Columbia University. She wrote poems, short stories, plays and a pantomime. She worked for some years at the Water Commission.

Louise Bennett, born in Kingston, Jamaica, went to Calabar Elementary School, St. Simon's College and Excelsior High School. She is an outstanding entertainer, and has published poems, songs and Anancy stories. She has been honoured with an M.B.E. and the Musgrave Silver Medal for her research and creations in Jamaican folklore.

Edward Brathwaite, author of *Rights of Passage, Masks* and *Islands*, and plays for children, is a History lecturer at the U.W.I. He was born in Bridgetown, Barbados; educated at Harrison College and Cambridge University. He was an Education Officer in Ghana for many years. Recently he went as a Commonwealth Scholar to England, where he obtained his Ph.D., and organized the Caribbean Artists Movement, which has published a journal called *Savacou.*

George Campbell has published a volume of his own poems, and was a prominent contributor in *Focus*. He was closely associated with the Jamaican Independence movement of the 1940s. He afterwards went to live in New York.

H.D. Carberry is a Jamaican barrister, who was born in Montreal, Canada, of West Indian parents. He went to school in Jamaica at DeCarteret School and Jamaica College, and afterwards went to Oxford University.

Frank Collymore, born in Barbados in 1893, taught English at Combermere School for very many years, and since 1943 has been an Editor of *BIM*, a magazine of West Indian writing. He was honoured with an O.B.E. in 1958, and in 1968 with an M.A. from the U.W.I.

Dennis Craig is a Guyanese from Georgetown. He is a Senior Lecturer in the Department of Education, U.W.I., who has also taught at Kingston College and Mico Teachers' College.

A.N. Forde, teacher, public administrator, General Manager of the Caribbean Broadcasting Corporation, was born in Barbados and educated at Harrison College, and afterward at the University of Southampton. He is one of the editors of *BIM*.

Nicolás Guillén is a Cuban, and a leading poet in the Afro-Cubanist movement in the 1920s and 30s.

A. L. Hendriks was prominent in broadcasting in Jamaica for many years. He was born in Kingston, Jamaica and went to school at Jamaica College, and Ottershaw College, in Surrey, England.

Ken Ingram, a native of St. Ann's Bay, Jamaica, now Librarian at U.W.I., was educated at Jamaica College, and went to England a few years ago on a Commonwealth Scholarship.

Evan Jones, a Jamaican, who taught in the U.S.A., has now settled in England where he writes scripts for television and films. He was born in Hector's River, East Portland, and attended Munro College.

Edward Lucie-Smith was born in Jamaica where he lived until he was 13 years old. He now lives and works in England as a highly successful poet and critic. He went to school in Jamaica, then in Canterbury, England, and finally read History at Oxford.

Basil McFarlane is a Jamaican journalist, son of the late J. Clare McFarlane who was Poet Laureate and a major influence on earlier writers in Jamaica. He was educated at Jamaica College and Calabar High School.

Claude McKay, born in Clarendon, Jamaica in 1890, left for the
U.S.A. in 1912, and died in 1948. He established for himself an
international reputation as a novelist and poet of the 'Negro
Renaissance' of the 1920s in the U.S.A. His poems about
Jamaica include *Constab Ballads, Songs of Jamaica*, and his
poems of nostalgia, written after he went abroad. He was
awarded a Musgrave Medal by the Institute of Jamaica.

Mervyn Morris is one of Jamaica's leading poets. He was born
in 1937, went to Munro College, University of the West Indies,
and then to Oxford University as a Rhodes Scholar. He was
Warden of Taylor Hall, U.W.I., and is now a Lecturer in the
English Department.

Daisy Myrie, was born in Richmond, St. Mary, in Jamaica, a
member of the talented Baxter family. She was educated at
Wolmer's Girls' School, and worked for some years in the X-ray
Department of the Kingston Public Hospital.

Alma Norman is a Canadian who taught in Jamaica at Short-
wood Teachers' College and at Calabar High School. She is
married to a Jamaican, and they now live in Canada.

Barnabas J. Ramon-Fortuné was born in Trinidad in 1917. He
has lived and worked there as a clerk and reporter for a short
time, and then as civil servant for over 30 years. He retired
recently to write full time.

Tom Redcam is the pseudonym for Thomas Henry MacDermot,
who has been called the 'father of modern Jamaican writing'.
He was born in Clarendon in 1870 of Irish ancestry, and died in
Britain in 1933. He had been a teacher, journalist, and editor of
Jamaica Times. He was posthumously made first Poet Laureate
of Jamaica for the period 1910-1933.

W. Adolphe Roberts, born in Kingston, Jamaica in 1886, was
educated by his father who had been a silk merchant in China,
and a clergyman and penkeeper in Jamaica. He was an author,
journalist, patriot, and founder of the Jamaica Progressive League

of New York (1936). He established a branch of the Leauge in Jamaica and was its President from 1937 until 1940. He died in 1962, and his ashes were placed in the Mandeville churchyard in Jamaica.

Dennis Scott was born in Kingston, Jamaica in 1939. He went to Jamaica College and the U.W.I., and has taught in Trinidad and in Jamaica. He dances with the National Dance Theatre Company, is active in drama as a playwright, director, actor, and teacher, and also broadcasts.

Sir John Squire, English poet, critic, and editor, was born in 1884. He read History at St. John's College, Cambridge, and was Literary editor of the *New Statesman*, and founder of the *London Mercury* in 1919, which he edited until 1934.

Derek Walcott was born in St. Lucia in 1930. He has published collections of poems, the first when he was eighteen years old. He has written plays, and is the founder and director of the Theatre Workshop in Trinidad, which is now his home. He went to school at St. Mary's College, Castries, and to the University of the West Indies, and then taught in Jamaica, St. Lucia, and Grenada.